Easy Christmas Time for Alto Saxophone

With Piano Accompaniment

Arranged by Stephen Duro

Chester Music
(A division of Music Sales Limited)
8/9 Frith Street
London W1V 5TZ

This book © Copyright 1999 Chester Music
Order No. CH61524 ISBN 0-7119-7679-1

Music processed by Allegro Reproductions
Cover design by Ian Butterworth
Cover photograph by Ron Sutherland
Printed in the United Kingdom by
Caligraving Limited, Thetford, Norfolk

CD orchestrations and production by Paul Honey
Solo Saxophone: John Whelan

Contents

ANGELS FROM THE REALMS OF GLORY

Traditional

Moderately bright

MISTLETOE AND WINE

Music by Keith Strachan
Words by Leslie Stewart & Jeremy Paul

Moderately

DECK THE HALL

Traditional

Molto rall.

MERRY CHRISTMAS EVERYBODY

Words & music by Neville Holder & James Lea

JINGLE BELLS

Traditional

Moderately bright

WHEN SANTA GOT STUCK UP THE CHIMNEY

Words and music by Jimmy Grafton

Moderately

Easy Christmas Tunes
for Alto Saxophone

Alto Saxophone part

Arranged by Stephen Duro

Chester Music
(A division of Music Sales Limited)
8/9 Frith Street
London W1V 5TZ

ANGELS FROM THE REALMS OF GLORY

Traditional

Moderately bright

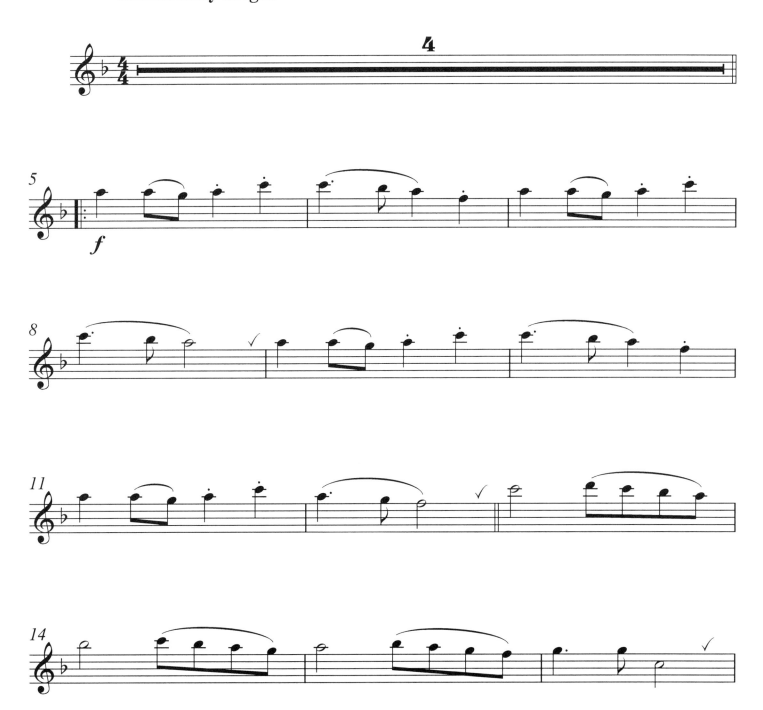

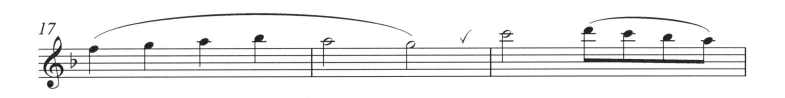

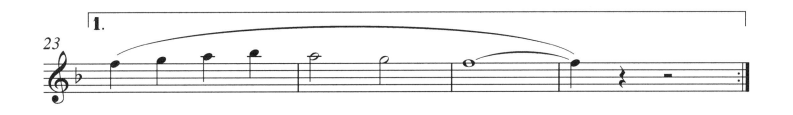

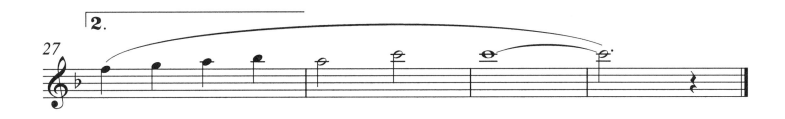

MISTLETOE AND WINE

Music by Keith Strachan
Words by Leslie Stewart & Jeremy Paul

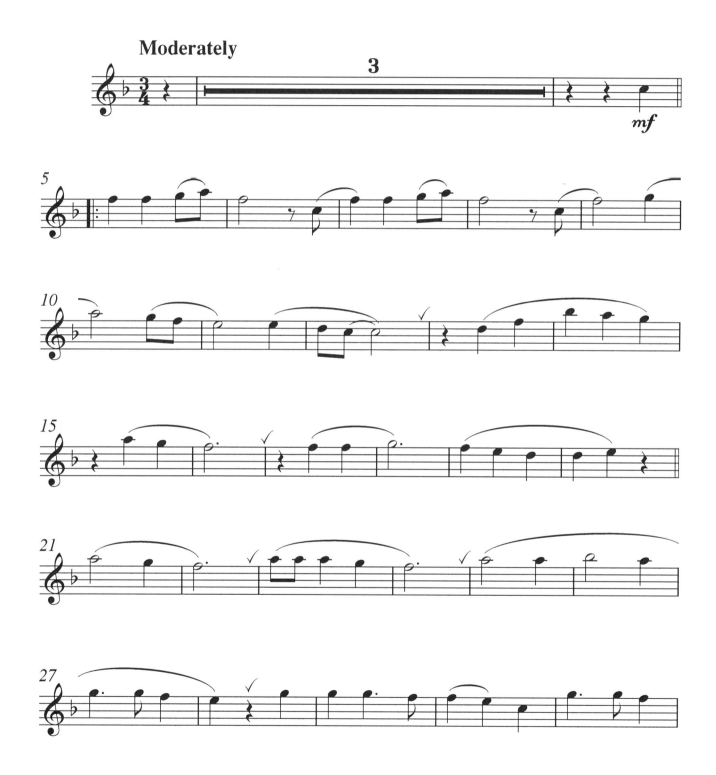

DECK THE HALL

Traditional

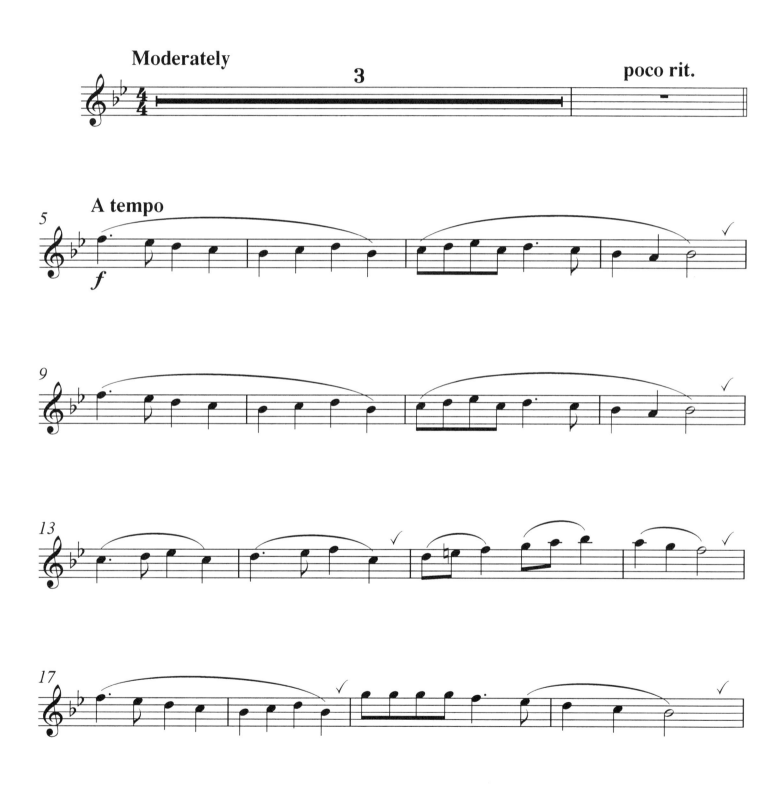

MERRY CHRISTMAS EVERYBODY

Words & music by Neville Holder & James Lea

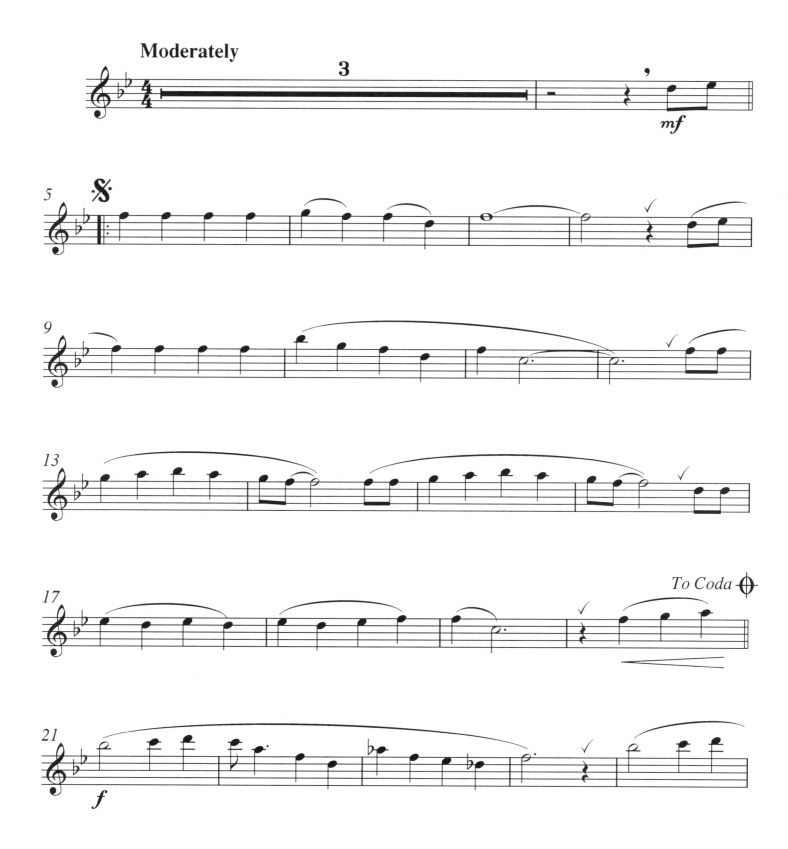

JINGLE BELLS

Traditional

Moderately bright

WHEN SANTA GOT STUCK UP THE CHIMNEY

Words and music by Jimmy Grafton

HOW FAR IS IT TO BETHLEHEM?

Traditional

I WISH IT COULD BE CHRISTMAS EVERY DAY

Words and music by Roy Wood

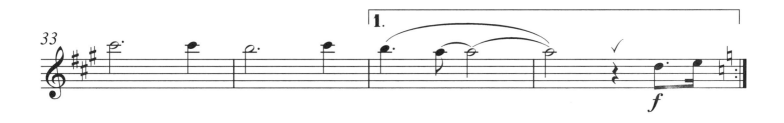

WE WISH YOU A MERRY CHRISTMAS

Traditional

A ROOTIN' TOOTIN' SANTA CLAUS

Words and music by Oakley Haldeman & Peter Tinturin

CHRISTMAS MEDLEY

Good King Wenceslas, Silent Night, God Rest Ye Merry Gentlemen

Traditional

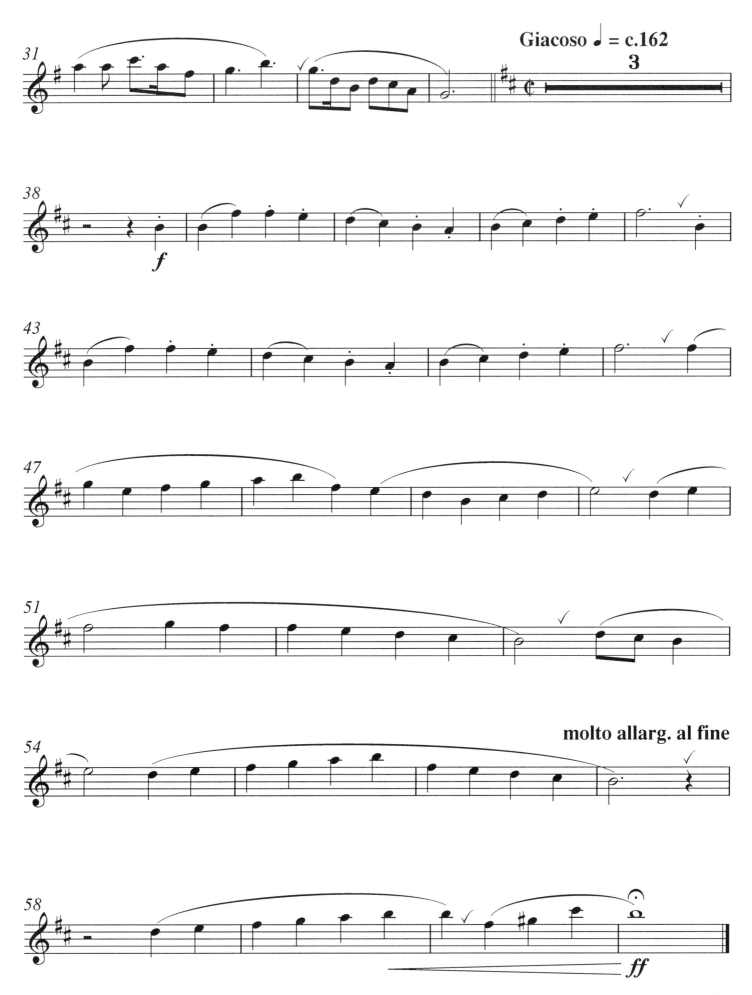

Contents

This book © Copyright 1999 Chester Music
Order No. CH61524 ISBN 0-7119-7679-1

HOW FAR IS IT TO BETHLEHEM?

Traditional

Moderately

I WISH IT COULD BE CHRISTMAS EVERY DAY

Words and music by Roy Wood

26

WE WISH YOU A MERRY CHRISTMAS

Traditional

Lively

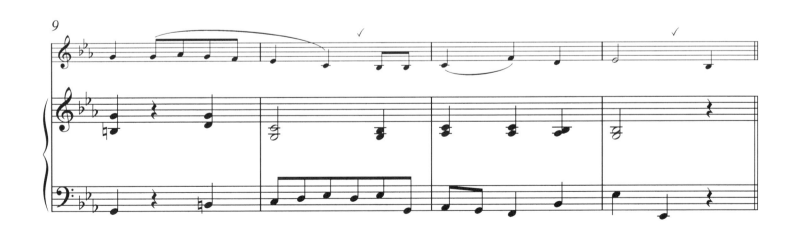

29

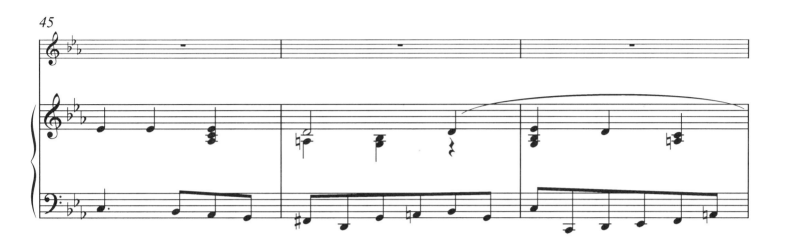

Ritardando

A ROOTIN' TOOTIN' SANTA CLAUS

Words and music by Oakley Haldeman & Peter Tinturin

Moderately bright

CHRISTMAS MEDLEY

Good King Wenceslas, Silent Night, God Rest Ye Merry Gentlemen

Traditional

Moderato ♩ = c.132

molto allarg. al fine

Also in this series

Easy Film Tunes

A selection of 10 great film tunes arranged for grade 2-3 players with intermediate piano accompaniment and a play-along CD with superb backing tracks.
Includes **A Time For Us** from Romeo and Juliet, **Colors Of The Wind** from Pocahontas, and **The Raiders' March** from Raiders Of The Lost Ark.

Easy Film Tunes For Alto Saxophone CH61468
Easy Film Tunes For Clarinet CH61469
Easy Film Tunes For Flute CH61470

Easy Pop Tunes

Ten classic pop tunes arranged for grade 2-3 players with piano accompaniment and play-along CD.
Includes **Thank You For The Music, Tears In Heaven, Sailing** and **Everything I Do, I Do It For You.**

Easy Pop Tunes For Alto Saxophone CH1296
Easy Pop Tunes For Clarinet CH61295
Easy Pop Tunes For Flute CH61294

Easy Classic Tunes

A selection of the greatest classical pieces arranged for the grade 2-3 instrumentalist with intermediate piano accompaniment and a superb play-along CD.
Including **Pavane** by Fauré, **Air On The G String** by Bach and **Toreador's Song** by Bizet.

Easy Classic Tunes For Alto Saxophone CH61521
Easy Classic Tunes For Clarinet CH61520
Easy Classic Tunes For Flute CH61519

Chester Music
(A division of Music Sales Limited)
Exclusive distributors:
Music Sales Limited, Newmarket Road, Bury St. Edmunds, Suffolk, IP33 3YB